One's Wedding

A DIARY

One's Wedding

A DIARY

MICHAEL O'MARA BOOKS LIMITED

First published in Great Britain in 2005 by
Michael O'Mara Books Limited
9 Lion Yard
Tremadoc Road
London SW4 7NQ

A CIP catalogue record for this book is available from the British Library

ISBN 1-84317-158-9

1 3 5 7 9 10 8 6 4 2

Designed and typeset by Design 23

Printed and bound in Great Britain by Cox & Wyman, Reading, Berkshire

EDITOR'S NOTE

Rescued from the compost heap at Highgrove in the nick of time, just as its 100 per cent organic recycled pages were starting to disintegrate, this startling journal was presented to the publisher by an established contact who had acquired it from 'an impeccable source'.

Is this the personal journal of the Prince of Wales? Were his ideas, dreams and desires really discarded and left to rot? Did whoever dumped the diary consider the Prince's innermost thoughts and feelings about his marriage to be worth no more than a handful of mulch?

Judge for yourself . . .

28th January 2005

It's still so hard for one to believe it has finally come — after all these years and all the unpleasant talk in the press — all the doubts and worries. On my very desk as I write is Camilla's note accepting my proposal of marriage. It is a lovely, warm note outlining how carefully she had thought about taking on the 'job' before humbly accepting. Too sweet really. Odd though; I don't actually remember asking her to marry me. Normally, I remember really important things like that, but there we are; I suppose one is getting on a bit. If she hadn't remembered to say 'Yes! Yes! Yes!' in writing the day after my proposal (copies to Mummy and the Archbishop of Canterbury), things could have become really embarrassing.

Funny how one suddenly changes one's mind about things like marriage. I was dead against it until a few days ago — in fact I found my little list of 'wedding pros + cons' a few pages back in this diary:

PRO

C. will stop whingeing about it

CON

It would mean getting married

2nd set of in-laws

First go at marriage a bit of a shower

Would have to find new mistress

29th January 2005

I didn't tell C. but I need Mummy's permission if this wedding thing is going to happen. My God! What if Mummy says no — what would I say to Camilla? No, mustn't think about that. Anyway, I couldn't get an appointment to see Mummy until June (so snooty, Mummy's secretary, it's 'Charles who?' and 'Prince of anywhere in particular?' Humph!) — so I've drafted a note:

Your Majesty (Mummy),

I know you are awfully busy with the steeplechase season in full swing and having to read 'Spotty' Blair's latest plans to ban everything normal country folk love, but I really need to ask a special favour for myself and another person.

I'm sure you never believed all that silly gossip about me and Camilla

Parker Bowles. Do you remember her? She was C. Shand, the daughter of 'Stinky' Shand. Her great-grandmother provided important services for your great-grandpapa. I know you haven't read the papers since 1992, but for some time Camilla and I have been considered an 'item'. We were photographed together at the 'Dead Fox Ball' in January and all the papers printed it on the front page.

Apparently, one proposed to Camilla last week (I believe C. copied you in to her acceptance) and one would look a very soggy pudding indeed telling Camilla that one's mummy wouldn't allow it.

This is so important, Mummy, Your Majesty, so please, please, please say yes. I will be so good from now on. I promise to be nice to the dogs (no more 'Corgi and Bess' jokes) and I will cheer for your horse at Ascot.

30th January 2005

Mummy seems v. keen on one's wedding.
I got this warm response:

FROM THE DESK OF THE THIRD UNDER-SECRETARY
TO HM THE QUEEN

HRH The Prince of Wales
Clarence House

Her Majesty The Queen has asked me to pass
on to you the following answer to your recent
request:

Yes.

I am, etc.,

I suppose it could have been more personal, but she is a busy woman (this is castration week at the Royal Stables).

Good news was quickly followed by bad, though. Mummy's third under-secretary rang to inform me that C.'s title is to be Duchess of Cornwall. (Apparently, I am the Duke of Cornwall! I always thought that was some other chap, but it was me all along!)

I thought it best to give C. this news over the phone — a very wise decision. Her response: 'A bloody duchess! Fatso Fergie is a bloody duchess! What's wrong with Princess Camilla? Your bloody sister is a princess and she's not even married to a prince!' etc. etc. I took this to mean that C. was not pleased, so rang the third under-secretary to ask him if

Mummy would promote C. to Princess. 'Over Her Majesty's dead body' was the response. So I rang C. with the good news that she gets to be a princess when Mummy passes on. C. soon pointed out that I had not really thought this one out. 'When Mummy is dead, you will be King, yes?' (There was no denying this. C. had got straight to the nub of the issue.)

'What do we normally call the King's wife — you know, the lady who sits on the throne next to her hubby the King?'

I wasn't expecting this query on royal nomenclature, with the result that I hesitated long enough for C. to answer her question herself.

'She's called the Queen, dummy. They go together like — ham and eggs, Cagney and Lacey, King and Queen!'

31st January 2005

Awkward conversation with Papa today:

'Why on earth would a man marry his mistress? What is the wedding ring going to get you that you are not getting already?'

'Well, it's just that she's been jolly loyal all these years, and I did propose, apparently.'

'Well, if QEII has given it the thumbs-up, what should I care? Mind you, this means that you will need a new mistress.'

'But I've already got Camilla!'

'Yes — but she's going to be your wife in a few weeks, which means you will have no mistress. So you'd better start looking now. At least you can get a younger model with less mileage on her, eh?'

1st february 2005

A fortnight ago when one was feeling rather depressed and with no one to talk with it suddenly occurred to me — what one needs is advice from 'Dear Dolly the Agony Aunt', whose column, so Pelk tells me, is a favourite feature of one of the tabloid newspapers. Cleverly disguising one's writing style in a working-class manner, one dashed off the following:

Dear Dolly,

I have been walking out with my bird for thirty years. I have been sweet on her all this time and the feeling is mutual, know what I mean?

Recently I had a note from my bird accepting my proposal of marriage but I don't remember asking my bird to marry me. This worries me.

The wedding is scheduled to be held in a few weeks' time. My Mum and Dad are dead against it and I am getting cold feet. What should I do?

Yours in desperation,
Gloucestershire Man

Here is Dolly's reply, as it was printed in her amusing newspaper:

COWARDY CUSTARD MAKES A MEAL OF WEDDING

Dear Man,
Call yourself a man? You've kept this poor woman dangling on a string for thirty years. A woman who has stood by you for the best years of her life without the simple comfort of a wedding ring on her finger.
You don't remember proposing? You are just trying to avoid commitment – you pathetic twerp!

As for your Mum and Dad – grow up, buster; a man your age shouldn't be tied to Mummy's apron strings. Tell them to mind their own business!

My advice to you is: put some woolly socks on your cold feet and hotfoot it to the altar.

A careful reading of Dolly's response leaves one in no doubt that one must do one's duty by Camilla whatever the consequences. I must stand on my own two feet, be a man for a change, and do exactly what Camilla and Dolly tell me.

2nd February 2005

Camilla had faxed me a list of suggested invitees to the wedding reception. Headed 'Initial Thoughts', the list contains approximately six hundred names. Working through it, I could see most of the Beaufort Hunt, including two of Camilla's favourite hounds, but what really caught my eye was the entry 'Mr and Mrs David Beckham.'

When I phoned to challenge her about this she said, 'They would be wonderful guests. He's the captain of England's footie team and she's posh.'

'Surely she's just a scrubber from Essex,' I said.

'No, her <u>name</u> is Posh. Posh Spice from the Spice Girls.

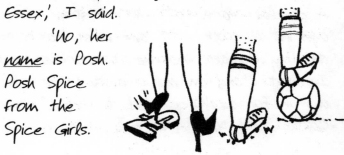

They are _the_ couple. They're more popular than you are!'

'Darling, a recent poll showed that whooping cough is more popular than I am. Beckhams or no Beckhams, you are going to have to cut at least five hundred names from your list.'

'Well then, you will have to cut five hundred names from your list, meanie.'

'I've only got twelve on my list,' I protested.

'You've made me cut five out of six. You do the same.'

'But that only leaves me with two!'

'Darling,' Camilla said sobbing, 'you've asked me to break the hearts of five hundred of my closest friends, and you complain about only ten.'

My face flushed with shame. How could I be so selfish, especially when C. is being so reasonable?

3rd February 2005

Had the most awful dream last night. I was backing the Land Rover out of the garage at Balmoral when I heard a sickening 'thump, thump' under the wheels. Hopped out to inspect and found, to my horror, one of Mummy's corgis flat as a pancake and no longer of this world. I was speechless with worry when my police minder, Carstairs, said, 'I'll sling it into the back of the Land Rover and we'll bury it in the woods, sir. Her Majesty's got so many of the little blighters, she'll never miss one.'

Off we went to the woods. I insisted on digging the grave myself as a way to expunge the guilt. But I hadn't moved three spadesful of earth when out of the hole popped a kilted genie.

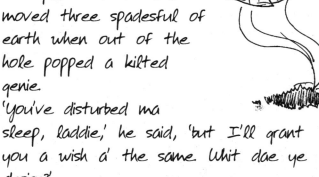

'You've disturbed ma sleep, laddie,' he said, 'but I'll grant you a wish a' the same. Whit dae ye desire?'

'Can you bring the corgi back to life?' I asked.

'No, I canna dae that,' said the wee man. 'Try again.'

'Well then, can you make Camilla more beautiful?'

The genie stroked his beard for a moment, and then said, 'I think it might be easier tae have a go at the wee dog.'

4th February 2005

C. on the buzzer this a.m. wanting to know whether it's to be St Paul's or Westminster Abbey.

'I'm glad you asked that question,' I said. 'I have no idea what the answer is but it's such an intelligent question, and so timely.'

'Perhaps you should ask someone, someone in authority, Puddle, and then we might have the answer.' ('Puddle' is C.'s amusing nickname for me. 'Puddle, as in shallow and wet,' she loves to say.)

But whom to ask? I'm sure that snotty fourth under-secretary knows, but why should one have to ask such a personal question, about one's own life, of a person who travels by bus?

I decided to ring Papa.

'Aged one, C. wants to know if it's to be St Paul's or the Abbey for the upcoming nuptials.'

There was a silence. I sensed steam coming down the phone line.

'Charles,' said Papa

'Yes, Papa,' I shot back, quick as a flash.

'How many state weddings do you suppose Mummy had?'

'Approximately one,' I answered, fairly sure of my ground on this one even though I wasn't at the ceremony.

'And how many state weddings do you suppose Grandpapa had?'

'I think the total is one in this case as well.'

'Are you beginning to see a trend here, noodlehead? If you must marry this Shand girl it will be behind closed doors at Windsor Castle. You know how busy your mother is — the flat-racing season begins in April, and anyway, damn it, we have other fish to fry. Low key is how Mummy wants to play it. The whole thing will be over in fifteen minutes and then you can get back to chatting with your marigolds. A local official from the Town Hall will do the honours. Same chap who fined Annie £1,000 just because one of her pursuit hounds took a lump of flesh from the nethers of some over-sensitive child.'

'But where will we put all the guests, the Dimblebys and their cameras?' More steam came down the phone line.

'There won't be any bloody guests – no horticulturalists, no half-baked philosophers and no retro-architects – just family. And that bloody boy of yours had better be sober and sans armband.'

End of conversation with angry parent.
I do wish I could speak with Mummy
occasionally. I'm sure she would be
more understanding. On the other hand,
the last time she phoned (1993, I think
it was) she uttered only four words:
'Pull your socks up!' It's all very well
for them to decide on a private
service, but who is going to tell C.?
Muggins, that's who.

    (Note to self: break news to C.
on a non-riding day. We don't want a
riding crop in her hand at that
moment.)

5th February 2005

'A wedding is no amusement but a solemn act, and generally a sad one.'

So wrote my great-great-great grandmama, Queen Victoria, some 150 years ago. She's bang-on if my experience is anything to go by. At least it raises the spirit about one's predicament to remember that Victoria refused to turn up to several weddings amongst her many progeny. And when she did make the effort it wasn't much fun: she wore black at her daughter Victoria's wedding and insisted that the bride do so as well.

Perhaps black should be the colour for one's wedding also; Camilla is certainly at her most fetching in ebony. On the other hand, if we make black the theme, Harry might turn up in an SS uniform! I think these questions might be left to Camilla.

To bed, somewhat sad.

6th February 2005

Edward on the blower — on the make as usual. 'Look Charles, I know the wedding do is flying under the radar — sotto voce, oui? Nevertheless there is an opportunity here for a very big hit — especially in the US market. The lack of the usual TV spectacular on the wedding day will leave the Yanks drooling for a big dose of purple satin and blue blood, are you with me bro? Here's the pitch — a two-hour TV film: *Camilla — My True Story*. Straight from the horse's mouth, if you'll pardon the expression. The story's got everything — girl meets boy; girl loses boy; girl marries wrong boy; girl pinches right boy from wrong woman. It's got great passion, secret assignations, love on horseback! We'll clean up! You and the Duchess get £500,000 up front and 20 per cent of the residuals; are you with me?'

Of course, I had to throw cold water on the boy. 'Edward, you know Mummy won't allow it. She hates it when we do TV. She wouldn't even let me talk about propagating pansies on Gardener's Question Time.' (Note to self: make sure Edward is body searched for miniature camera on big day.)

7th February 2005

Camilla is truly entering into the spirit of twoness. She's suggested a new coat of arms for us to signify an eternal bond. I suggested a joining of the Prince of Wales feathers with a pair of pink roses, but C. was leaning towards something equestrian I was initially a bit miffed when Camilla faxed me her design for our new coat of arms.

I phoned Camilla straight away in a bit of a temper. 'Darling,' I said in my sturdiest voice, 'your design seems to be a bit one-sided. Your saddle, your riding crops, your helmet. Where are the Prince of Wales feathers?'

'They are under the helmet,' C. explained. 'That's why you can't see them. But they are there.'

8th February 2005

One would have thought selecting the date for one's wedding would be a straightforward affair — open diary, examine until satisfactory day is identified, announce date. But no; this apparently simple detail has become the cause of the most extreme bad feeling:

I have been in tears thrice. I pray Camilla has not suffered also but, sensitive soul that she is, I fear her spirit has been bruised.

It began when Camilla suggested (I suppose decided would be a better word) that the great day would be the 5th of May. I had nothing important on for that day (the visit from the Suttons Seeds rep. could be put back a week) so I put it to the third under-secretary (I actually spoke to his secretary; he was having a massage at the time).

An hour later the third under-secretary's secretary rang back to say that the 8th of May was out because my brother Andrew was opening a school for exotic dancing in Brighton on that day; what is more, Andrew has booked all three royal helicopters for the day (apparently Andrew was giving some of the exotic-dancing students a go at handling his joystick as a reward for matriculating — at least I think that's what he said).

This was just the beginning! I can't bear to record the entire to-ings and fro-ings, but at least ten dates were suggested and shot down by:

Mummy — conflict with corgi mating (apparently she and Papa like to watch in order to see that it is done 'properly');

Princess Michael of Kent — washing her hair that day;

Prince William — previous engagement (had agreed to hold hand of girlfriend as she had diamond stud inserted in navel);

and so on!

Finally we arrived at the 3rd of May — everyone happy at last, but I had no sooner put the telephone down after giving Camilla the good news than the third under-secretary rang.

'The 3rd is out,' he said with admirable brevity.

'But that is virtually the only day in May that . . .'

'May is out,' he interrupted.

'But Mummy agreed,' I protested, wishing I had said 'Her Majesty' rather than 'Mummy.'

'This comes from higher up than, er, "Mummy".'

My blood froze. 'Spotty Blair?'

'Correct. The PM has decided that there is only one day in the year for the wedding, and that day is the 8th of April this year.'

'Well, there is always next year, I suppose,' I said, feeling a curious sense of relief.

'No. The PM has decided the wedding is a good thing. He can't wait a day later than the 8th of April.'

'Well that is very sweet of him, but there won't be enough time.'

'Sir!' the under-secretary butted in. 'Are you aware of another important event taking place this year, apart from your little wedding?'

I can't say I liked his tone, but I had a stab at an answer.

'The footie World Cup?'

'No sir. The non-gardening pages
of the newspapers have been full of
speculation about the date of the
general election. The odds-on favourite
is early May.'

'But surely we could have the
wedding in the months after the
election; June or December, for
example, or in 2006, or 7?'

'Have I not already mentioned,
sir, that the PM is very keen on the
wedding? He feels that it will keep
the tabloids occupied with speculation
about Mrs Parker Bowles's wedding frock
and other crucial issues surrounding your
happy day, thus keeping details such as
the unpleasantness in Iraq out of the
headlines. In short, sir, he feels that
your wedding will guarantee his re-
election.'

'Surely Mummy won't stand for

this?' (Damn! I said 'Mummy' again.)

'Mr Blair mentioned the upcoming review of the Civil List when he telephoned sir. He became very sympathetic to our position on royal taxation when we agreed to the 8th of April for your wedding.'

'Stitched up in a way not dissimilar to the proverbial kipper,' I suggested stoically.

'Well put, sir,' I heard him say, before the dialling tone.

9th February 2005

Camilla telephoned.

    'I'm giving you a ring because you haven't given me a ring, geddit?'

    I didn't.

    'Engagement, silly. We're engaged and engaged men buy their loved ones wonderful big rings to show their devotion.'

    Oh really? I'd rather forgotten about that. Camilla mentioned that with her rather chunky fingers only the largest stone would do. Since Mummy bought the sparkler last time around I thought I'd phone the third under-secretary, but when asked if Mummy might fork out for an industrial-sized rock he pointed out that Her Majesty felt that she'd got little return on her first investment in finger furniture on my behalf, and therefore I might reach into my own jodhpurs for the cash on this occasion.

    I searched deep into my memory

banks but I could find no experience of paying for something.

'Should I infer that your silence betrays a reluctance to go the retail route, sir?'

Before I could answer his insolent question the third under-secretary pointed out that in the basement of Buckingham Palace there were three drawers full of engagement rings which my family had been using and reusing for eons. I quickly called for my car and four motorbike outriders to take me the few hundred yards from Clarence House to Buckingham Palace.

The third under-secretary was there to meet me. Pulling out one of the drawers he asked what size was required. He put this question with the unpleasant smirk he reserves for those moments when he knows I haven't a clue.

But I was one step ahead of the pompous little twerp on this occasion.

Barely containing a sneer, I slipped from my inside jacket pocket an envelope. 'This size,' I said, handing the packet to the somewhat abashed official.

I smiled a mildly superior smile as he opened the envelope and removed the contents.

'A sausage, sir?'

'Yes. A sausage identical in size and shape to the ring finger of my betrothed,' I said triumphantly. 'Perhaps we can now get on with the selection.'

The rings in the first two drawers were all much too small.

'Let's look at drawer three then, under-secretary.'

'But sir, that drawer is full of costume jewellery.'

'She will be wearing a costume of some sort, man. We are not interested in nudist jewellery.'

'You don't understand, sir. Costume

jewellery is fake. The stones are made of glass.'

'So everyone would know it wasn't a real diamond?'

'A person of taste could tell, sir.'

'Well, that's all right then,' I exclaimed.

We finally selected a ring featuring an enormous glass 'diamond' which had been specially made for the then Prince of Wales (later Edward VII) on the occasion of a fancy-dress party in which he appeared as Catherine the Great of Russia.

Ring Selection Pros and Cons

PROS	CONS
Really big (huge, even)	Worthless.
Really cheap (free even).	Tacky
C. won't know it's fake	Fake

10th February 2005

TO C. ON THE OCCASION OF ONE'S ENGAGEMENT

Thirty years or more it's been
With you who'll always be my Queen.
Into my life on steed you trotted
And won my love; I was besotted.
In early days I had your hand
But let it slip, my darling Shand.
I sought adventure on the sea,
Then among men, Whoopee! Whoopee!
And while I plied the ocean's rolls
You went and married Parker Bowles.
Through many years of pain and sorrow
We waited for this bright tomorrow.
And though by some you are still
loathed,
you are my pumpkin;
my betrothed!

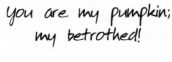

11th February 2005

Camilla on the blower this a.m. re music on the big day. She suggested some more modern music than one's family is used to on these occasions.

In fact, she's written some words to the music of one of today's top groups (one loves the effortless way C. keeps up with all the latest in the music scene — some people are just naturally 'with it'). The music is from a song called 'She Loves You' by an orchestra called 'The Beatles' (apparently there is a pun in there somewhere). I'm sure that it will go down a treat. It beats dear brother Andrew's suggestion that Schubert's 'The Trout' should be played as Camilla walks down the aisle.

For posterity, here are Camilla's lyrics to 'She Loves You':

He loves one, yes! yes! yes!
He loves one, yes! yes! yes!
And I've got the ring
That shows he really cares
One may not be brand-new
One's been down the aisle before -o-ore
But he's got history too
And he's no looker that's for sure -u-ure
But he loves one
And we're saying our 'I dos'
He loves one
And you know that is good news!
He loves one yes! yes! yes!
He loves one yes! yes! yes!
You could say I've got the top man in the land
I should say I've got the Prince right in my hand
Yes, yes, yes, Yes, yes, yes, yes.

12th February 2005

All this wedding nonsense is very nervous-making. How one yearns for those blissful days of one's first marriage. We were so carefree, so in love, so sex-mad – Camilla and me. I could strangle that Morton man! I count those years on the scale of happiness by the AM and PM clock: AM is After Morton and PM is Pre Morton. In our secret, PM years, meetings with C. were blissfully illicit and so sexy. I could come and go as I pleased with Camilla. (Gosh, I've just realized that statement could be considered quite rude!) No need for long chats about the expense of keeping up appearances etc. from C., no demands for a dress allowance. Hot sex and sympathy is the way I would sum up the years with her, PM.

But After Morton! Divorces all over the place; Mummy furious; private secretaries insisting on 'photo-opportunities' with William and Harry twice a week to show what a loving father one is. In short, the AM years could be termed (to paraphrase Mummy) Anni Miserabiles. Of course, darling Camilla saw it differently: 'Now that everyone knows, darling, there is no need to hide.' Thus began the time when our meetings contained neither sex nor sympathy but much about the cost of C.'s household, the need for extra staff, PR people, bodyguards, hair stylists. I don't know where the money comes from (which is just as well because, if I did know or care where the money comes from, it could be jolly annoying). AM means that, when one goes to the opera, Camilla comes too so one must be careful not to cry during the last act of La Traviata.

13th February 2005

Camilla slammed the telephone down on me again this morning. She's been trying to quit the fags and the experience has changed her demeanour from polite surliness to something bordering the Hitlerian. How I regret complaining about the ashtray breath and the cloud of nicotine-tinged smoke which accompanied her every movement. The worst of it is the hopelessness of the effort — she simply needs to smoke. Her gardener, Baxter, has told me that she's taken to walking along behind his tractor, inhaling the diesel fumes. Last Wednesday when I popped into her sitting room there was the most sick-making smell. On examining the ashtray I found to my horror that she had been smoking her nicotine patches!

FOURTEENTH OF FEBRUARY -
ST VALENTINE'S DAY.

As has been one's custom since one's
first wedding, I have made a valentine
for C. with my own hand. Before 1981,
one was able to send a footman out
to buy a large pink thing for Camilla
on this day which celebrates love and
lovers, but after one's first wedding
circumspection was the order of the
day — hence the handmade efforts.

No need for secrecy now, of
course, but C. wouldn't be pleased with
something from Woolworths — too spoilt
by the Bard of Balmoral:

Whatever Love Means

Whatever 'love' means
One's surely got it
You bring one sweet dreams
One's cream is clotted
One's soaring heart beams
Young Cupid's shot it
Whatever love means
Our bond is knotted.

15th February 2005

Very upsetting call from Wills this a.m.
'What on earth has happened to your
nose, Pop?' he said, to one's great
bewilderment. 'And your ears. They're all
red. You look like something from the
top of a totem pole, or one of those
crazy masks the natives of New Guinea
wear to frighten away evil spirits. Luce
the Goose [his latest flame, Lucinda
Paddington-Station] says you need some
pancake make-up. And you might consider
surgery before you face the cameras when
you marry Brigadier Parker Bowles's wife.'
    Wills can be so cheeky. The trouble
is I can't tell him off because he
outranks me. Apparently I am merely the
Prince of Wales, which is rather a small
country, while William is the Prince of
England, a much larger country. (Note to
self: must find unembarrassing way of

asking fourth under-secretary if Wills's theory of princely rank is correct.)

Cut to the quick by Wills's comments about one's visage, I called in my valet, Pelk

'I am going to ask you a question and I want an honest answer. In fact, I must ask you to be brutal, if necessary.'

He nodded rather nervously.

'Do you think my nose and ears are unusually red? And do you think my head would be put to better use as a device for frightening away evil spirits?'

← DOES THIS BIT BELONG TO ANNE?

MINE

HIS

Silence ensued as Pelk stared at the floor. The valet was perspiring visibly.

'Come on. Give me the truth.'

'My wife and I were just sayin' the other day,' said Pelk, 'what delightfully distinctive ears you 'ave, sir, and a nose that sets you apart from other men.'

That made me feel a bit better, but nevertheless I thought a visit to Papa might help.

'Red ears and nose?!' he shouted. 'Come over here and stand next to me in front of the looking glass.' I obeyed.

'Now look carefully. Are your ears and nose any redder than mine?'

They were clearly not, and I said so.

'Well then, there you are. You have a perfectly normal glow of health about you. It's the contents of your head, if any, that worry me.'

16th February 2005

Camilla on the blower this a.m.

'I had that nice woman from *Hello!* on the telephone, Puddle. We really need to decide whether to go with them or *OK!*'

'I'm not sure I follow you.'

'A day late and a shilling short as usual, Puddle. Let me explain: these days, when famous people get married they sell the exclusive rights to the wedding pictures to a glossy magazine, usually *Hello!* or *OK!* For example, when Michael Douglas married that chubby Welsh girl, *OK!* gave them a million pounds and published page after page of gorgeous photographs, carefully touched up so that even Michael Douglas, who must be in his eighties, looked glamorous.'

'Darling,' I interrupted, 'you must know Mummy won't allow it.'

'But Puddle, we can't turn down a million pounds! Think of the things we could buy with that money!'

'Money, precious? We don't use money in the family firm. If it were not for the fact that Mummy's face is plastered all over the stuff, we would have no connection with money at all.'

'But how do you buy . . . ?'

'We don't buy things, you silly dear. We simply say we want something and it appears — like my new Aston Martin.'

'But someone must have bought it.'

'When you've been in the family a few years, you will learn not to ask that question. In my view it's none of our business how these things turn up; somehow, a grateful nation supplies our every earthly wish. Don't rock the boat is my advice.'

NOT TO BE ROCKED!

17th February 2005

Received a note from the third under-
secretary as follows:

E II R

FROM THE DESK OF THE THIRD UNDER-SECRETARY
TO HM THE QUEEN

HRH The Prince of Wales
Clarence House

Subject: Honeymoon arrangements,
Duke and Duchess of Cornwall

Would you like me to put some people on this, or have you got it
all in hand?

Stupid man. Shows how much he knows about royal tradition. I sent him a sharp note back reminding him that one always has one's honeymoons on the Royal Yacht *Britannia* and that there are **no** exceptions to this rule!

(Later today)

Oh dear, rather unpleasant conversation with Camilla when I revealed my honeymoon plans.

'Won't it be romantic, darling? Just you and me and a couple of hundred sailors and marines. Oh, and the staff...'

'You moron! *Britannia* is a tourist attraction in Scotland, and has been for years. Don't you remember your mother crying her eyes out when they towed it away? And anyway, why do you think I would want to spend a week with you on a leaky boat.

Too wet altogether!

Think again, Charlie.'

18th February 2005

With any luck I will wake up tomorrow to find that today was nothing but an unpleasant dream.

Things began well enough. Camilla telephoned, finally accepting Windsor Palace (or 'the Heathrow Hilton', as she calls it) as the venue for the wedding and bunfight. My satisfaction at this small victory lasted precisely ten minutes when the third under-secretary rang up.

'Slight hiccup with the venue for your joyous day, sir. It seems that for you to marry in the castle it must become licensed. The trouble is, once it is licensed, the general public can use it as well for weddings for three years. I think it would be wise to point out this drawback to Her Majesty and the Duke, on the off chance that they might mind.'

When I phoned Papa with this news
there was a bit of an eruption.

'A licensed premises for three
years! Shall we rename the castle "The
Queen's Head" and start serving pub
grub to visiting heads of state? You
will have to find somewhere else to
marry this Parker Bowles
woman – perhaps she has
a spare palace.'

Not ten minutes
after Papa slammed the phone down
with a mighty click, brother Andrew
phones with his commiserations.

'Bad luck, Chaz. Second wedding,
very tricky. That's why I've always
avoided the second stroll down the
aisle; more complications, more wives.
Have you considered Las Vegas? I
understand they do quickie weddings
there without asking questions. For a bit
extra they can do you an Elvis

Presley-style wedding. They could play "You Ain't Nothin' But A Hound Dog" as Camilla walks up the aisle.'

Very amusing. By the end of the day we had come down to two choices of venue, a Thames disco boat, or Windsor Town Hall. But we found out that the disco boat had been booked by Freddie Starr, so the Town Hall was decided on by default.

I won't try to describe the conversation with Camilla when I broke the news. Let me just say there were plenty of tears and much sobbing and wailing — Camilla was quite upset, as well.

Various church chappies going on about how the wedding might be illegal. Daily Mail and Telegraph suggesting the whole affair might have to be scrapped. (Odd, this thought not nearly as upsetting as one might expect.)

20th February 2005

I think my limit of forbearance has been reached. I just can't believe it has happened! My cushion is gone. Vanished! I had to go in the car all the way from St James's Palace to Holborn without my cushion. I really can't describe the agony. Both the driver and my police officer swear that the last time they looked my cushion was in its place, just waiting   for my lower back to be pressed against it. My loyal little cushion; where are you? Too upset; can't write more.

21st February 2005

An all-time first today — a phone call from Spotty Blair. Amongst many other drawbacks, this rare pleasure took place at 6 a.m.

'I'm having breakfast with President Bush. He's taking some exercise between his Cheerios and his home-fries. He described his exercise as "taking his bowels for a walk". Don't you love that directness? Anyhoo, I called to reassure you that I am on your side.'

Was it the early hour that confused one?

'Which particular struggle finds you on one's side, Prime Minister?'

'Why, the wedding struggle, of course. Surely you've noticed that quite a few pundits in the Tory press are calling for a cancellation of your wedding plans because it's illegal.'

'Well yes, Prime Minister, I have seen these arguments and I must say they are very persuasive. In fact, I am going to phone Mrs Parker Bowles this morning to chat about a postponement – until things get sorted out.'

'Now, your Royal Highness you must not do that. [Sounding a bit panicky here, I thought.] Let me reassure you that there is no way they can stop the wedding taking place on the 8th of April – NO WAY! [shouting here]. As you may know, we in the government think the wedding is a very good thing. I trust Her Majesty has informed you that a certain arrangement has been made between Buckingham Palace and Downing Street over this issue. In any case, the worst that can happen is that you would have to marry

Mrs Parker Bowles again in a few years if the courts find the wedding illegal.' 'But that would mean we would be living in sin for that period.'

'And what have you and Mrs Parker Bowles been doing for the past twenty years?'

I had never thought of those wonderful years with Camilla as sinful, but His Spottiness had an unanswerable point. There was a pause at the PM's end of the line and I nearly rang off when a new voice continued where Spotty had left off.

'Your Princeship, this is the President of all the United States speakin' to ya. I just wanted to add my congratulations to every other Tom, Dick and Tony's on your upcoming nup-tur-all celebrations. That's a great little filly you're hitchin' your wagon to. I was just sayin' the other day to my wife that your Camilla would look real good sitting on a Texan saddle — "A seat you can't beat" was the way I put it.

'Anyhow — you want privacy on your honeymoon, you come on down to Crawford, Texas, to my spread. You and the new Mrs Prince will love it. I understand you like organic food — we got tons of organic — we got liver, we got kidneys, we got calves' brains; hell, we invented organic down there. Well, I gotta go see that sumbitch Chirac now. This aint gonna be fun; this fella don't know how to obey orders like your boy Tony. Anyhow, you gimme me a call when you wanta use the ranch. I'll call down 'n tell'm to dust off the best sheets. So long, pardner.'

I was about to say goodbye when the dial tone commenced to buzzing. What a kind offer.

An amusing thought crossed my mind after the conversation with President Bush. What if Spotty Blair decided that his adored master in Washington deserved a knighthood in the next honours list? How I would love to do the honours.

'I dub you Sir Dubya.' Must tell C.

All the way to Highgrove and back without my cushion. Is this the Brave New World? Is this one's future existence? I'm not sure that I can bear it.

22nd February 2005

'Binky' Beef-Wellington on the blower, wanting to know who the best man will be on the blessed day.

'Me,' I shot back without a pause. My witty retort worked on Binky, who laughed and snorted for a full five minutes.

'It's just that the best man needs to have a few decent jokes to break the ice. All the more important when the crowd is a bunch of bishops and commie politicians,' said Binky. 'I've got a suggestion or two for you. These are tried and tested and I've fine-tuned them for the occasion.

'Joke number one: "It seems that our bridegroom, the Prince of Wales, was once on an ocean liner which sank in the middle of the Pacific. He managed to make his way to a small island. A large dog and a pig also managed to reach the

island. After a few weeks on the island, Prince Charles began to fancy the pig. Unfortunately, every time he approached the pig, the dog would growl menacingly.

'"This went on for several months until a day when our favourite prince spotted a small vessel approaching the island. When the little boat landed Charles saw that it contained none other than Camilla wearing only a skimpy bikini.

'"Camilla sauntered sexily over to Charles, kissed him and asked if there was anything he needed. 'Yes. You can take that dog for a walk,' said Charles."'

Binky snorted and choked for another five minutes after this effort. I can't see what on earth is so funny about dog-walking. Mummy does it every day without so much as a smile.

'Surely you can do better than that, Binky?'

'I've got a real belter for you Charles. The key is to personalize these things, as you will learn.' Binky cleared his throat of any debris which might interfere with the delivery of his 'belter.'

'Well, the best man says, "I'm not saying that Prince Charles is an elderly bridegroom, but the other day he had to visit a doctor in Harley Street with a certain complaint.

'"The doctor welcomed the Prince and said, 'That will be one hundred pounds in advance. Now tell me, what is your problem.'

'"Charles gave him the money and said, 'Doctor, I'm having a lot of trouble with my short-term memory.' The doctor considered this for a moment and said,

'That will be one hundred pounds in advance.'"'

Strange how one's mind keeps going back to those wonderful days of the 1980s when Camilla and one were both married to other people and so happy. Pity it all had to change.

I especially remember Sunday nights sitting stealthily, covered in darkness, in a lane behind Camilla's house. No driver, no detectives, just me, on the prowl. How my heart leapt when I saw the headlights of Colonel Parker Bowles's car suddenly pierce the darkness and ease away into the night on his way back to London. Almost silently, and with no lights, I would slip my car into the forecourt. What followed was bliss — so passionate, so sweet — so naughty.

And Camilla was so gay, so carefree. 'Isn't it funny?' she would say. 'My hubby's title is Silver Stick in Waiting. But you, sitting quietly in your car outside, are my Silver Dick in Waiting!'

23rd February 2005

Carstairs had the gall to 'replace' my cushion. When I got into the car this morning this . . . thing . . . was there on the back seat.

　　'Carstairs. What on earth is this?'

　　'It's a cushion, sir; just like the one you lost. Just what you need for your back.'

　　'This thing is _a_ cushion; not _my_ cushion, Carstairs. I want the Palace combed until it is found!' I really must be firm on this issue.

Things to remember

1. Get wedding rings (or does someone do this?). Note: ask third under-secretary if there is another drawer in Buckingham Palace filled with wedding rings of dead Windsors.

2. Best man? Is there one at these town-hall affairs?

3. Town Hall chap. Does one need to make his acquaintance? Is he titled? Camilla will be upset if not.

4. Can Camilla bring her dogs to the ceremony? I said I would ask. Whom does one ask?

Third under-secretary on the horn.
'No need for Binky Beef-Wellington to
cancel his dental appointment after all,
sir. We won't be having a best man on
the blessèd day,' he said with his
customary cynical cheeriness.

'Just as well really,' I
responded. 'It might be better if Wills
and Harry stand for me. Keep it in the
family.'

'That won't happen either, sir. The
boys would rather stay out of this
one.'

'What do you mean, "stay out of
this one"? They are going to be at the
wedding, aren't they?'

'They're going to be there all
right. They just don't want to be seen
to be too close to you and Brigadier
Parker Bowles's former wife.
'Actually,' he continued, 'no one wants
to be close to you at the service, sir.

'We've had to devise a sort of cordon sanitaire between you and your bride and everyone else. Even the official who is performing the ceremony has insisted that you and Mrs Parker Bowles stand at least four feet from him.'

'Is one a leper? Has one contracted a communicable unpleasantness?' I asked.

'It's just that the wedding isn't everyone's cup of tea, sir, especially amongst the family. Her Majesty's refusal to have the ceremony in any of her several houses is one of many indications that you and Mrs Parker Bowles are not exactly Beau and Belle du Jour. I can't tell you how many members of the family have asked to be "just outside the frame" for the wedding photographs.'

Can't say I blame them — I'm not looking forward to the wedding photographs either. Standing there in a top hat, ageing Lothario with pancake make-up on nose and ears. Pushing sixty.

Still, Camilla is keen, and will no doubt carry all before her (especially me).

Found it!! That stupid Miss Beagle had sent cushion to the dry cleaners. I was so worried the cleaning process might have ruined it, but we took it for a drive and all was well. I felt so calm and composed with my cushion pressed against my lower back I now feel so much more confident about facing all this wedding business.

24th February 2005

More nonsense in this a.m.'s papers: 'Charles Must Not Be King' and 'Arise King William'.

How one laughs. The idea that one would want to be King. I'd rather run an all-night petrol station. The trouble is, William doesn't want to be King either and Harry doesn't even want to be a prince. (He likes to call himself 'the rich kid formerly known as Prince'.) In fact, the only one of the family, at present, who wants to take the throne is Princess Michael of Kent. Why not? I say. It's not as if a bit of Germanic blood ever did any harm to the line. But Mummy abhors the idea and hopes that William might have a son willing to take the baton. If this fails, she has decided not to die. What a trouper!

I'M NOT FINISHED YET!

ER

Awful morning. Reception for world
champion Australian water-polo team.
Embarrassed myself straight away by
asking the team's captain if they have
lost many horses due to drowning. How
is one supposed to appear well informed
when one is not properly briefed?

   Tried one's best to liven up the
conversation with questions like 'How
long have you been Australian?' but the
affair was deadly dull, regardless.

   Home to find Camilla scribbling
furiously at my desk

   'A bit early to be writing your
memoirs, darling,' I jested.

   'I am writing my wedding speech,
Charles, and I am rather pleased with
it,' she replied.

   'But surely, precious one, you
know that the bride doesn't make a
speech at the wedding reception? I
think tradition has it that the bride's

father, the best man and the groom do the honours.'

'Get real, Charles! My father is eighty-eight years old and in no condition to make a speech. As you know, you are not allowed to have a best man, and as for you . . . well, you can't seriously be suggesting that anyone wants to hear you prattle on about organic architecture for twenty minutes?'

Strange how Camilla's conversation often reminds one of a door slamming. Conceding the point, I said, 'If you must make a speech, Camilla, there are some very strict rules by which you, as a member of the family, must abide. Firstly, you must not make any jokes of a religious nature.'

At this point Camilla scored out a few lines from her speech.

'Naturally, you must not make

any jokes that might be considered rude or in doubtful taste.'

Her black pencil ran through several paragraphs.

'And no swearing, of course.'

She swore as she crossed out several more lines.

'And under no circumstances must you make the slightest reference to Mummy retiring.'

At this Camilla rose and tossed her entire speech into the fire.

CAMILLA'S SPEECH FILED HERE

25th February 2005

How long has it been since one has
been able to write these words?
– 'What a splendid day!' Indeed, it
reminded me of the good old days of
the 1980s in that one was on one's
own the entire day (not counting the
eighteen staff, of course). Camilla was
having a fitting at the dressmakers, and
I was to make a quick visit to an
organic Mars Bar plant in Scotland.

     The great news was that one was
able to get hold of one of Mummy's
helicopters for the day. It was only
after we were aloft and on our way to
Auchtermuchty that I removed from my
bag a very special hat. When I put it
on I could see that Pelk and Carstairs
were mightily impressed because they
stared at it, open mouthed.

     'I see you are admiring my
special hat. It was made with a fox

we killed during a hunt with the Beaufort last year. The tail hanging down at the back, and the charming head with its beady eyes popping out at the front, are rather fine, don't you think?' All the people of Auchtermuchty were quite bowled over by the hat as well.

The mayor said, 'I canna say I've iver seen the likes o' it.' Later, the head of the organic Mars Bar plant made it quite clear that my hat had been a great success. 'Your Royal Highness, I have to admit that your hat has been the main talking point of the visit. How on earth did you ever get the idea to wear it?'

'As usual, I can take no credit for the decision since it was entirely Camilla's idea. You see, when I told her this morning that I was visiting Auchtermuchty, she said, very firmly, "Wear the fox hat!"'

26th February 2005

Very annoying, this digging up of old stories about oneself by the cheaper papers in the excitement surrounding one's wedding. I'm surprised Mummy's subjects still find it interesting after all these years. There is one story, though, which even I still wonder about. A short time before one's first wedding, the tabloids reported that one had a 'night of passion' with a 'mystery' woman in Mummy's train. The papers suggested at the time that the woman might have been one's first fiancée.

After the Morton book came out the same newspapers identified Camilla as the shadowy female.

The strange thing is, after all these years, even I do not know the identity of this person. It was one of my 'train' nights in 1981. I had been doing this since the age of twelve; using

Mummy's train to play conductor. With the train safely berthed in a siding I would pass through the carriages punching the tickets of invisible passengers. Since adulthood I always played this game in the dark because Mummy's advisers thought the public might find it all a bit silly for the Prince of Wales to enjoy himself in this way. (Although I can't imagine why; whom was one harming?)

In any case, on this night I was making my way through the sleeper section when a figure approached out of the darkness, embraced me and whispered, 'You know you want it, and I know it too. Now is the hour.' With this I was hoisted into the sleeping compartment for a night of wild and, I must say, rather unusual love-making. As dawn approached my mystery lover stole off with a kiss and a firm-handed pinch of one's bottom which left a bruise for a week But who was it? Much too tall for Camilla, and much too athletic and muscular for the first wife. Also the voice much too husky for either of the above.

For months afterwards, on meeting any of the women in my circle, I would pull an imaginary train whistle and say 'choo-choo' whilst winking suggestively. But this brought only quizzical looks from the baffled ladies.

So, nearly twenty-five years later, I still have no idea who my partner was in this passionate train journey to nowhere. But I shall never forget the thrill. I believe I received what the army chaps call 'a good seeing to'.

Off to sleep — perchance to dream?

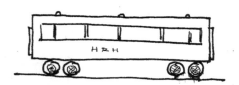

27th February 2005

Counting the moments until my Australian trip. What a joy it will be to get away from all the sniping, coarseness and mean-mindedness — although, to be fair, Camilla doesn't always behave like that. The pressure of the wedding must be getting to her.

But Australia beckons for me — all by myself for ten days (well, I will be bringing a skeleton staff of fifty-two). Mustn't forget cushion! I couldn't endure the trip without it and no doubt there would be unfair comments in the press if we had a repeat of the 'hairbrush incident'.

Such a fuss over nothing. I was touring Canada when, on arriving in Vancouver, it was discovered that my hairbrush had been left in Toronto.

Obviously, it was impossible to continue with ones duties without the brush, so it was decided to send an RCAF fighter jet on the 4,000-mile round trip to fetch it. I still don't understand what could be considered wrong about it. I wanted my brush, there were any number of jet fighters sitting about gathering dust. It isn't as if Canada were under attack from the Red Baron.

This is what one means when one says one is being treated unfairly. I am sure that if some ordinary citizen who didn't happen to be the Prince of Wales, a bus driver for instance, sent an RAF jet to collect his hairbrush no one would have minded at all.

The great thing about this trip is that one is enormously popular in Australia. I'm sure the streets will be lined with adoring Aussies hoping to catch a glimpse of one. We could hardly control the crowds on my last tour, with the first wife of course. One could feel the adoration! I am looking forward to another strong dose of it.

28th February 2005

Off to Australia. What pleases one most about this trip is that it enables one to show one's scientific side, and help the Australians to save their environment at the same time.

Years ago, I read that the millions of sheep and cattle in Australia and New Zealand were releasing dangerous quantities of methane gas into the atmosphere, thereby damaging the ozone layer with their billions of farts. My great love for the lands 'down under' led me to discover the cure for Australia's, and indeed the world's, pollution problems.

In tests at Highgrove, I have shown that it is possible to collect the methane from the animals' farts by connecting large balloons to their bottoms. The methane collected can be used as a fuel for cars, electricity plants, and so on, thus nearly eliminating our dependence on fossil fuels.

Of course there were problems to overcome: initially we attached very large balloons to the sheep's bottoms. Unfortunately, this resulted in some of the smaller animals floating off into the sky (two were shot down during the pheasant season by the Duke of Peebles, who cried, 'A brace of Cheviots! I've shot the bloody bladders out of their arses!'). We soon overcame these difficulties and today all the royal cars are fuelled by FF (fart fuel). What one will propose to the Australians is that they exploit my experiment on a national scale. If

every sheep and cow in the Antipodes is fitted with a fart balloon those countries will soon need no oil at all, and will at once stop destroying the ozone layer with the farts of their animals.

Under my plan, huge zeppelins will travel round Australia collecting the farts from the bum-balloons. These lighter-than-air transports will be filled with methane which will both keep them airborne and fuel their gas-powered engines. Cow farts will be the world's first self-transporting fuel! One cannot wait to see the expression on the face of the Aussie Prime Minister when I reveal my scheme.

1st March 2005

Long, boring flight to Australia. Thank goodness for cushion pressing snugly against one's spine. Somehow flying thousands of miles away from England gives one a feeling of lightness; of release. One made the long flight to Australia before one's first wedding and felt the same emotions; the same thoughts.

What if one made a run for it, just disappeared into the Australian outback? Lord Lucan is probably there now, playing poker with sheep ranchers. Fraught with problems though. Alone, one could disappear easily enough, but what of one's fifty-two staff? No doubt one or two of them would write home to a wife or mother and give the game away. And there is the problem of pay. Would they all disappear with me into the outback, knowing there would be no way that one could continue paying the salaries? Most of them would, gladly one is sure, but again, one or two might rock the boat. A hopeless dream, one fears.

Tired now; sleep coming. Last night as I dropped off my mind went back, as it so often does, to the strange night of love in the railway carriage. As one dropped off one whispered 'Good night, sweet stranger,' and I thought a voice answered, 'Good night, sweet prince.'

March 2005

C. so upset that our wedding news has caused the cheap papers to haul out the so-called 'Camillagate' tapes once more. Surely the nation has seen enough of this embarrassing conversation? All that Tampax business! Good Lord! But what makes one cringe is the pure banality of it all:

He: Don't want to say goodbye.
She: Neither do I, but you must get some sleep. Bye.
He: Bye, darling.
She: Love you.
He: Bye.
She: Hopefully talk to you in the morning.

He: Please
She: Bye, I do love you.
He: Night.
She: Night.
He: Night.
She: Love you for ever.
He: Night.
She: Night night.

And so on for another twenty
minutes. The whole business
would be entirely forgettable
for me if it were not for
the two outstanding mysteries
of the tapes:

1. How did the newspapers get
hold of them?
2. Whom on earth is Camilla
talking to?

March 2005

Casting my eye along Camilla's suggested wedding list I saw, along with the usual shops like Harrods, Fortnums and Purdeys, something called 'Lasha's Leather Goods'. When asked, she told me that 'Lasha's' is where she gets her 'special' riding crops, as well as other items for our private use.

Fortunately, Camilla saw the sense of my argument that drawing attention to our mutual interest in discipline at this moment might not be wise. I suggested mail-order shopping for leather goods in future (with plain brown wrapping paper!).

March 2005

Third under-secretary on the blower, yet again.

'Thought you might like an update on the wedding, sir.' He said this so cheerfully I knew, at once, it was further grim tidings.

'What now? Have they changed the venue to a disused coal mine in Poland?'

'Oh no, sir. As of this moment Windsor Town Hall seem happy to give you fifteen minutes of their time. It's Her Majesty, sir. She won't be attending.'

'Oh no! I suppose it must be some constitutional issue which prevents her attendance — or security worries.'

'No, nothing like that, sir. She was happy enough to attend the ceremony at home, but she won't leave the castle. You see, sir, Her Majesty has had an excellent tip as to the winner of the

2.15 at Wincanton on that day, and she wants to watch the race on the telly.'

'Can't she record it and watch it later?' I proposed, somewhat pathetically.

'It's more fun watching it live, sir. And she has a fiver on Wonky Willy to win.'

'Oh dear. More bad luck! Still, at least the rest of the family will be there.'

'You remind me of another little point, sir.' I steeled myself. The third under-secretary's 'little points' tend to be bone-crunchers.

'The only members of your family attending, sir, will be your sons. I can't speak for anyone else's family.'

He obviously didn't know that the only reason William and Harry are coming is because I threatened to withdraw their pocket money for a month if they don't turn out.

'Would you like the good news, sir?'

'One could certainly use a bit of that,' I said, walking straight into his next blow.

'Well sir, the small turn-out means we won't be needing the longer room of the Town Hall. This will save the taxpayer £250.'

'Oh, Mr Taxpayer will be pleased,' I replied, not without a certain bitterness, but the wretched fellow had rung off.

March 2005

Note delivered by page from Princess Michael offering to 'stand in for the Queen' at the wedding ceremony. The word 'cheek' scarcely describes it. She was the only member of the family whom one had not invited, and she is the only one who wants to come. Sad to admit it, but I actually considered this proposal for a moment – until I recalled the frosty looks C. gives her whenever they are in the same room.

Send polite letter to Princess M. thanking her for kind offer but gently refusing etc. etc.

You never know, she might be Queen one day.

March 2005

My valet reminded me that the photographs for my Christmas card need to be taken by the end of March.

'Surely we can use the same one as last year. The boys and I can't have changed much.'

'But sir, won't you be wantin' another person in this year's picture?'

'Another person? Why would we want another person? . . . Oh, right – Camilla! How could I forget Camilla?

This is going to be awkward, actually. The boys won't want to be photographed with Camilla, so that is out. However, if I send out a Christmas card with a picture of only Camilla and myself, the newspapers will claim, accurately in this instance, the boys are not over keen on the new stepmother. On the other hand if I pose with the boys but without Camilla, I will have to answer to her — a thought that causes a shiver to creep up one's spine.

I explained the problem to Pelk, who said, 'May I make a suggestion, sir?' 'Have you ever seen them billboards, sir, advertising big West End shows?'

'Of course, Pelk. Indeed, one has attended many such attractions.'

'Well sir, these billboards has photos of the main performers with their faces in stars. To show, like, they are stars themselves. Do you see what I am gettin' at, sir?'

'Why, Pelk, you are a genius. I see just what you mean. We take individual photographs of Camilla, William, Harry and oneself and place our faces in stars, just like the star which so fascinated the three Magi.'

Good man, that Pelk. Problem

solved. Here is my sketch showing the design:

March 2005

One was stunned into momentary silence at the sight of number two son perched on a chair at the breakfast table. True to form, he was in the oddest outfit — what looked like

evening dress, with tie askew. There appeared to be lipstick on his neck. Perhaps it is merely the style of the new Gothic revival one reads about.

No 'Good morning' or 'How are you, dear Father,' but instead, 'Got the tickets

for Klosters yet, Pop? I only ask because William and I might like to bring a couple of young females, chalet girls,

you know what I mean?' At this point he winked, somewhat

groggily one felt.

'Good Lord. I had forgotten all about our annual skiing holiday together. But what about one's wedding to Camilla?'

'That's OK, Pop, Camilla's never skied in her life, although the sensation of going downhill fast would not be new to her.' I sensed some unkindness in his words, but couldn't quite place it.

'Nevertheless, it would be impolite not to ask Camilla in the somewhat awkward circumstances.'

'Whatever. I'm off to bed,' said Harry as he disappeared up the stairs. But he'd only just had his breakfast. I asked the butler, Tetley, if he thought the boy might be ill.

'No sir. I expect he might be a bit tired; you see, he's just come home after a sporting night.'

'Rugby?' I asked.

'Rumpy pumpy, sir.'

march 2005

Rang Camilla to invite her to skiing jaunt with the boys.

'Skiing! A week before the bloody wedding?'

I sensed some unease on her part.

'But I thought it a good opportunity for you to bond with the boys,' I suggested.

'Charles, you know the boys can't stand the sight of me. And you know I can't bear children, especially when they're grown up.'

'Yes, I suppose they can be bit tiresome . . .' I began, somehow knowing that this conversation was about to come to an abrupt end.

'Charles, precious.'

'Yes, darling.'

'I won't be going to Klosters.'

'The boys will be so sad.'

'And Charles. Do you know who else will not be going?'

'No, my only one,' I lied.

'You won't, that's who. How do you think the wedding photographs would look with me in my beautiful outfit and you with a broken leg and a black eye?'

Her remarks betrayed her ignorance of the skiing scene.

'Darling, a person may break a leg whilst engaged in skiing but a black eye is out of the question.'

'If you turn up with your leg in plaster, I will supply the black eye.'

'I will take that as a "no"!'

March 2005

Camilla has given me a list of honeymoon spots which have taken her fancy. After the skiing débâcle I decided to give her carte blanche.

Note to third under-secretary:
Would you please look into the feasibility of a two-week jaunt for myself and my wife (for so she shall be) after the wedding in the following countries:

Kenya (I understand that the shooting of many animals is still allowed here). China (I understand that shooting more or less any animal, including some classes of humans is still kosher here). Also Papua New Guinea and Australia.

Very quick response from third under-secretary:

To: HRH Prince of Wales

Subject: Honeymoon site

Naturally, sir, where you and Mrs Parker Bowles honeymoon is entirely up to yourselves, but perhaps I should remind you of the great unwritten rule of your family. Briefly, the rule is that no member of the family should ever visit any country where Prince Philip has been within the past half century.

Might I give Your Royal Highness a few examples of why the welcome mat has been withdrawn?

Kenya – when presented with a gift by a sweet local lady, your father responded, 'You are a woman, aren't you?'

China – famously, the Duke warned some British students that they would get 'slitty eyes' if they stayed in China too long. Another comment: 'If it has got four legs and isn't a chair, if it has got two wings and isn't a plane and if it swims and isn't a submarine, the Cantonese will eat it.'

Papua New Guinea – to a backpacker who had been trekking in the hinterland, 'You managed not to get eaten, then?'

Australia – here your father refused to touch a koala bear because 'I might catch some ghastly disease.' He asked an aborigine, 'Do you still throw spears at each other?'

I hope, sir, that this is helpful. Do not hesitate to let me know if you have any further honeymoon ideas.

Somehow, I see Balmoral beckoning.

march 2005

Went to bed last night feeling so old.
All this bother seems to be ageing one
beyond one's years. That might explain the
most frightful dream.

For some reason, one was sitting
on a bench in Hyde Park crying one's
eyes out. A stranger approached and said,
'What's the problem, old fellow?'

One raised one's reddened eyes and
held out one's wizened hands and said,
'That's a good question. I've got all the
wealth in the world, and the love of a
wonderful woman, I've got everything.'

The stranger patted my hand and
asked, 'So why are you crying old man?'

'I can't remember where I live!'

This morning C. informed me that in the
absence of a speech at the reception
she would add to the entertainment by

doing some 'rapping'. This is not something to do with a séance but, apparently, a form of music.

This aint some tacky piece of bling
This here's my royal wedding ring
And you who said the bride was mingin'
Just listen to that choir singin'
Its C and C right down the line
'Cause we're each other's Valentine
To you who say these vows aint cricket
I'm tellin' you where you can stick it
The Duchess of Puke Street
I've been dubbed
But Charlie's my man and I'm
well loved
So give me some slack and stop
that jive
Cut out the crap and give me five
Now you be my homies if you aint fools
And join me in shoutin' 'Camilla rules!'

Finding one's mind sifting through the events leading up to one's proposal of marriage to Camilla (which I still can't quite remember)

More and more one's thoughts focus on the Grosvenor-van Cutsem wedding. Rum time then. One family or the other decided that Camilla, since she is not a member of the royal family, must sit two rows behind one in the church. Camilla, of course, unhappy.

'Poor you, darling,' I consoled. 'I would understand perfectly well if you decided not to attend the wedding at all.'

'You are so sweet, darling,' she replied. 'But there is one other little thing.'

The word 'little' got me worried.

'And what is that, precious?'

'You wouldn't think of going without me, would you?'

To one's great credit, it took no time to work out the correct answer to this question.

'Why, of course not, darling. Wouldn't dream of it. Much rather do a bit of gardening'

'No. Not gardening, dear. We must make an official visit, you and me. I know, we can inspect the Black Watch together.'

'Rather awkward, pumpkin, at this short notice'

'I know, darling, but just put fifteen or twenty of your best people on it and I'm sure they will sort it out.'

Easy for you to say, I was thinking, when Camilla continued. 'Of course, there is a way of avoiding all these worries in the future.' A certain queasiness came over me at this point. 'If we were married all these problems would disappear — poof! your friends would have to treat me in the proper way — as a superior. Oh darling, you don't want to travel first class while I'm back with the luggage, do you?'

Interesting image. I was rescued from this awkward conversation by the timely intervention of Pelk, but it sits in one's mind as the first time the unpleasant 'M' word spilled from Camilla's lips.

Only a few months would pass before I would ·lose a mistress and gain a wife. A fair swap?

March 2005

Short note from the King of Bongaland (which is, I believe, a small island in the South Pacific):

No doubt you remember the major international incident when you forgot to invite My Blessed Highness to your first wedding. We are happy to forgive and forget. We look forwards to seeing you and your new woman at the Town Hall. No need to make a fuss; I will bring only thirty-four of my best wives.

Here's a first, a monarch who wants to attend one's wedding. Where are the red carpets when one needs them?

March 2005

At my first opportunity after the
exhausting Australia trip I decided to
take cushion for a run in the Aston
Martin. But horror, horror, the Aston is
absent from its place of honour in the
Highgrove garage.
After a hard grilling, one finally got
the story from Pelk

'It was Mrs Parker Bowles, sir.
She insisted on having a go. Said you
would want it to be exercised. Ten
minutes after she set off the police
was on the line — she'd ploughed into
a chestnut tree on an S-bend near
Tetbury.'

With a mixture of fury and deep
sadness I rang up Camilla.

'So-ooo sorry, sweetie. The man
from Aston Martin said it was a write-
off which, I believe, is a bad thing.'

'It is a very bad thing indeed,'
I said, trying to find a stern tone.

'But darling, you won't miss it,' she
continued. 'It was the most useless
Aston Martin ever — they really sold you
a pup. There was no machine gun at the
front like the one in the film. I was
searching for the ejector-seat button
when the car went off the road.
Apparently there isn't one on yours. You
seemed to have the cheap version,
Charles, with none of the optional extras.'

I suppose Aston Martin will give
one a new one soon enough — the fully
equipped one this time, one hopes.

There is one great consolation:
thank God cushion was not in the car
when it went up in flames!

march 2005

A storming visit from Papa.

'Well, I hope you are happy. You've got the whole family rolling in the manure now, not just yourself. I told you at the time of the Grosvenor-van Cutsem wedding: you don't bring your mistress to weddings. You certainly don't marry your mistress. What would have happened if I had marr— ?. . .

'Well, forget about me. When a gentleman, much less a member of our family, marries his mistress, nothing but trouble follows. Look what happened to your Great-Uncle David — King Edward VIII, albeit not for long — he married that ridiculous American woman and ended up crouching at the dining-room table, barking for scraps like a poodle.'

Woof Woof

At this point one mumbled something about love. This was probably a mistake.

'Just because you love your mistress,' Papa interrupted, 'doesn't mean you have to marry her, you fool. What you do is buy them a diamond bracelet, give them a title, give them a bloody county! Anything but marriage! In our business, we normally have our cake and eat it. In your case someone else has got the cake, the wedding cake, that is, and she is also going to eat it – and you!'

Door slams; end of conversation.

ARCHITECTURALLY SOUND ORGANIC CAKE

March 2005

Mummy's — I mean, Her Majesty's —
third under-secretary telephones during
elevenses. He knows one hates being
disturbed during elevenses — which is why
he does it. Apparently I am to await a
visit from the third under-secretary —
something to do with 'security during your
forthcoming little jolly'.

'You're going to love this one, sir,' the
third under-secretary said jauntily when
he tipped up in my study an hour or so
later. 'We're off to see the military.'

   'Ah, the life of men among men!
The Household Division, I imagine? Are we
going for luncheon in the mess?'

   ''Fraid not sir. We're going to meet
Captain X, who's an expert from the
Regiment.'

   'Which regiment? There are still
three or four left, you know, despite

the best efforts of this government.'

'<u>The</u> Regiment, sir. You know —
hush-hush and all that. Think Hereford,
think black balaclavas, think stun
grenades, think . . .'

The penny dropped like a well-
killed grouse.

'Ah, got you, third under-secretary.
You mean the Speci—' The fellow cut
me off before I could finish.

'Precisely, sir. Them. We've given
him a room in Windsor Castle, and we're
to meet him there. The car's outside.
And yes, your cushion is in it.'

I insisted that Camilla is as much
in need of security as oneself, so we
picked her up on the way. This turned
out to be a rather poor idea.

When we arrived at Windsor we
were ushered into the East Gun Room.
Outranking everybody else, I entered
first, and as I did so an arm like
whipcord wrapped round my throat, a hand

grabbed a clump of my hair, and a gravelly voice said: 'Who the f**k are you?'

At that moment there was a loud crash. The hand holding my hair and the arm enclosing my throat relaxed as, with a low moan, my assailant slipped to the floor.

Nearly fainting myself, I heard another gravelly voice. It was Camilla.

'Oh, Charles you should have told me it was going to be so realistic. I've never had so much fun. Whom do we fight next?'

'Madam,' intoned the third under-secretary, 'you have just concussed an SAS officer, our leading expert in hand-to-hand combat. I should add that in the process you have destroyed a six-hundred-year-old Ming vase. The officer was trying to demonstrate to His Royal Highness that an attacker can strike at any time.'

This brought an end to our security

lessons. When the captain regained consciousness, I suggested that we have another lesson some day.

'We'll do you, sir,' he said. 'But if she comes,' pointing at Camilla, 'we want danger money.'

On the way home I learned that Camilla's friends are organizing a 'hen night' for her a few days before the wedding. One was instantly rather concerned that this was going to be one of those awful occasions when a group of baying middle-class slappers is entertained by a male stripper.

How ashamed one was to have suspected such a thing, when C. told me that the 'hen night' was in fact to be dedicated to a discussion of eighteenth-century English furniture. One only wishes one could be there oneself. It seems the ladies are getting the Chippendales in to give them a tongue-and-groove session. Camilla said she was looking forward to getting her hands on a stiff English joint.

With this new knowledge Camilla will, in future, feel a special thrill each time she pops her bottom down on a Chippendale.

March 2005

Brother Andrew on the blower. Raining in Southern Spain, no golf, what to do? — answer: ring Prince of Wales.

'Are you still going to marry the Parker Bowles woman, old fruit?'

With only the slightest hesitation, one answered in the affirmative.

'Your funeral, old stick. Personally, I'd say eighteen holes at La Manga are preferable to . . . well, you know. Still, if you insist on going ahead with this madness, Binky Beef-Wellington and yours truly have come up with a stonking plan for the stag night.'

Oh God, one thought, what madness could Andrew's idea of a stag party bring — topless waitresses, Fergie lookalike chorus lines? The idea filled one with horror.

But oh, how I underestimated the high-mindedness of my brother. Far from bawdiness and booze, what he had in mind was a cultural evening packed with innocent entertainment.

For what Andrew has suggested is an evening of Eastern European folk dancing. I didn't catch all of what he said, but Lapp dancing and Pole dancing were at the top of the list.

march 2005

Camilla on the buzzer this a.m.

'Charles, you know how you and your mummy have this royal warrant thing where you let various shops nail your coat of arms over the door?'

'Yes, of course darling, places like Purdeys the gunmaker and Hatchards' bookshop, very old and distinguished.'

'Then, darling, you wouldn't mind if I gave a few warrants of my own? – after we're married, of course.'

I could hardly refuse. What could be the harm in it, one thought. But later one received a fax from Camilla with a list of her warrants and a design for the shield to be placed above the shop doors.

1   Lasha's Leather Goods

2   Big Boy's Beefburgers

3   Rhodesian Ridgeback cigarettes (they are producing a
    new line: 'Camilla's Biggies, The High-Tar Ciggies')

4   Cammy Dolls

Puddle: an American company – Jefferson Brothers – want to sell a
Cammy Doll – a mini-me in my wedding frock. They are going to
produce a limited edition of only 2 million dolls – and I get a dollar for
each one sold (or 'a buck per schmuck,' as Mr Jefferson put it). C. xxx

At the foot of the fax, Camilla
had sketched her design for her own
warrant badge – rather a departure from
the usual coat of arms, one thought.

BY APPOINTMENT TO
HRH THE DUCHESS OF CORNWALL
MANUFACTURERS OF LEATHER GOODS
LASHA'S LEATHER GOODS LIMITED

March 2005

Edward on the blower this p.m.

'Whoa, is Mummy blazing! You are really in the bow-wow house this time, big brother.'

'Tell me something I don't know,' I said resignedly.

'She is specially steamed about picking up the tab for a wedding she is not crazy about, to put it mildly.'

'But what can one do, Edward? The wedding is now a fact of life. There is no going back. And anyway, who else is going to pay for it?'

'The taxpayer, you sap. Give me the word and I can get a lottery grant to cover all the costs.'

'But aren't those grants for the arts?' I protested.

'Yeah, the arts and entertainment. And if your wedding doesn't fall into the category of entertainment, then I'm a commoner. Now that it's taking place in the Town Hall the general public are free to gape at you and your new woman all they want. That makes it entertainment.'

'But the reception will be private,' I put in.

'Yeah, that's the only change we have to make. If we throw it open to the public (at a charge, of course) we will be eligible for a full grant. All the champagne you want, Rod Stewart providing the music, and all paid for by the bozos who buy lottery tickets. What do you say?'

'Mummy will be thrilled,' was the kindest thing one could utter.

March 2005

Camilla on the hooter

'Charles, you know all these army chaps who muck about on horses round Buckingham Palace and Whitehall and environs wearing kinky boots and a lot of tin plate?'

'You mean the Household Cavalry, darling.'

'Yes, I thought that's what they were called. Tell me, precious one, after we are married, these chaps will be, at least partly, my Household Cavalry too, won't they?'

'In a manner of speaking, I suppose they will, darling,' I answered, rather pleased to see Camilla taking an interest in traditional royal affairs.

'That means I shall have full access to the members of the cavalry, doesn't it, darling?'

'For what it's worth, sweet one, I suppose it does. But I don't know what on earth you can do with fifteen hundred guardsmen.'

'I'll think of something, sweetie.' That's what one loves about Camilla — she doesn't mind taking an interest in men's things.

March 2005

Highgrove, 2 a.m.

So late. Can't sleep. Sitting here in one's bedroom with only a small lamp. Big day coming on like a runaway train.

They say when times are tough you find out who your friends are. If so, how depressing. Mummy and Papa (and the rest!) won't be coming to the wedding ceremony. Andrew thinks it's all a great joke, Edward thinks of nothing but getting a TV contract out of the wedding. And Camilla! She's beginning to act like one's wife.

So alone. Wait a minute, what's that noise? Someone is creeping into one's bedroom. What? That firm hand . . .

It's you, the mysterious . . .

EDITOR'S NOTE: This is where the diary ends. Is it truly the wedding diary of Prince Charles? We may well never know the answer to that question. Nor is it likely that we shall ever discover the identity of the mysterious stranger who first appeared on the Royal Train twenty-four years ago. But will our hero find happiness in the arms of his long-time lover?

Of course he will.